MOVIE POSTERS
OF THE SILENT ERA TO COLOR

Illustrated by
REX SCHNEIDER

Notes by
CHRIS BUCHMAN

Dedicated to
William Cameron Menzies

PUBLISHERS, INC.
Owings Mills, Maryland

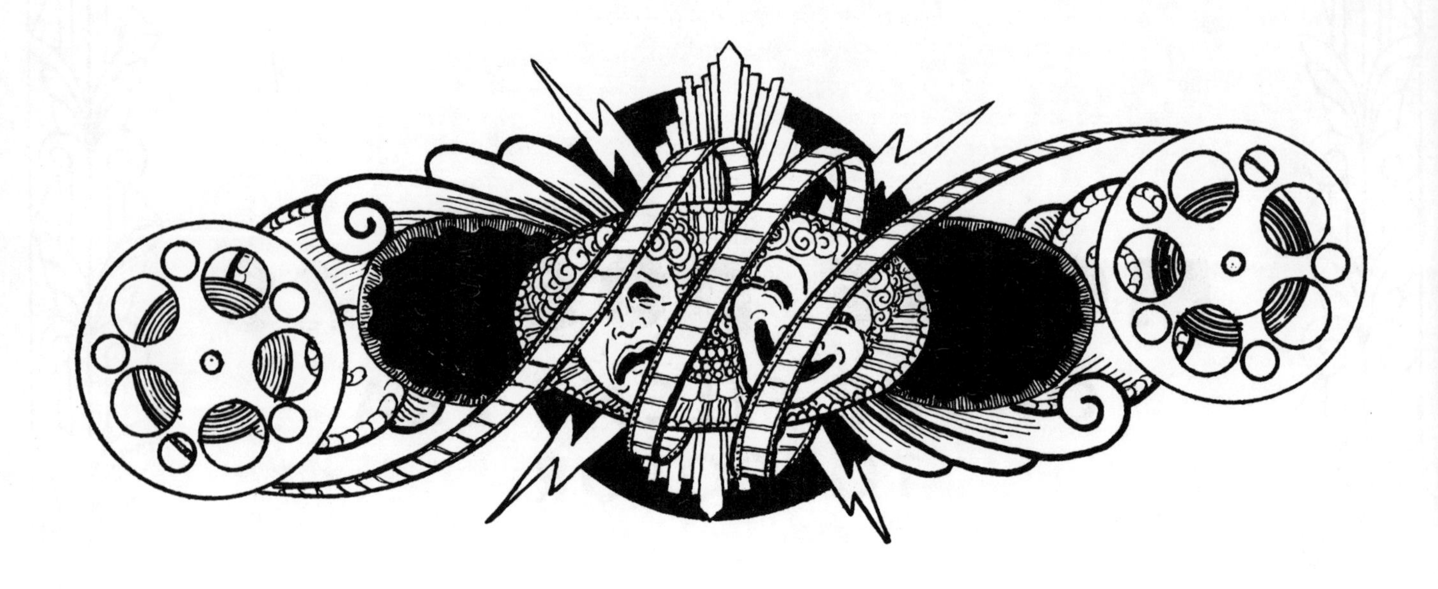

INTRODUCTION

For decades, connoisseurs have been collecting advertising art and theatrical posters of Henri de Toulouse-Lautrec, Maxfield Parrish, Alphonse Mucha, Aubrey Beardsley and John Held, Jr., while at the same time thumbing their aristocratic noses at the illustrators of motion-picture billboards.*

In fact, until about 1960, all of the contributing arts of the cinema were threatened with oblivion simply because there appeared to be no real interest in preserving film prints or original film negatives. If it had not been for the ceaseless efforts of the Museum of Modern Art, the Library of Congress, George Eastman House, the American Film Institute and individual archivists throughout the world, much of the ninety-one year history of film culture would by now be irrevocably lost.

The renaissance which began in the mid 1960s has been overwhelming. One surprising discovery after another has been made. Old movies are suddenly new movies and not museum pieces after all. It is no longer so chic to consider them camp or nostalgic curiosities. Finally, older works of art are not deemed nostalgia simply because they represent another era. Moreover, the interest in the older films is not confined to acting styles, directorial techniques, theory, writing or even to social mores of the past. There is an attentiveness to the contributions of the artisans and technical craftspeople whose names have become internationally known. Cinematographer Oswald Morris, composer Erich Wolfgang Korngold and costume designer Edith Head are but a few examples. William Cameron Menzies, the illustrious creator of brilliant set designs—to whom this book is dedicated—is yet another.

Just as the arts of the motion picture are now recognized and appreciated, so too are

*Traditionally, "billboard" refers to an advertisement for theatrical programs and/or a place to accommodate such public announcements, not the giant roadside billboards.

the impressive billboard graphics once displayed in and around movie theatres.

The posters not only reflect the atmosphere of the movies, but also provide a stimulating glimpse of the eclectic art styles of the various periods. Pre-turn-of-the-century European posters were either traditionally "theatrical" or somewhat circusy. The same is true in America between 1900-1910, although the form was more primitive. As the movies slowly evolved into popular entertainment, so did the elaborate nature of posters, as evidenced by the influence of Art Nouveau, with its swirling intricate lines, and Art Deco.

Art Deco is a recent term used to describe what, in 1910, was the beginning of the Modern Art movement. Art Deco was born out of Art Nouveau; that is, the delicate curved lines of Nouveau became formalized in geometric patterns. As the transition occurred (e.g., AFGRUNDEN), the appearance became mechanical (THE GENERAL) and angular (METROPOLIS) and finally, quite decorative (TWO TARS). Most Art Deco is derived from artists' preoccupation with the aesthetics of machinery; it also implies an emphasis on the two-dimensional nature of the visual elements.

Nouveau was still in vogue during the Deco period, as reflected in the posters for THE PRICE OF SILENCE and SALOME. To a lesser degree, abstract and expressionistic posters (e.g., DAS CABINET DES DR. CALIGARI) were also popular.

While we are beginning to recognize the names of the artists who created costumes and designed marvelous sets for the movies, very little or no information seems to exist concerning the persons who illustrated cinema posters. Artists rarely signed their names or were given credit for their work, and very few original posters have survived. Until recently, posters were displayed only in connection with the exhibition of the movies, after which they had to be immediately returned, and eventually destroyed.

Just as many movies survive today because "pirates" stole and illegally reprinted them, so the same is true of old posters. Those that exist belong to the public and are now worth small fortunes. In 1980, a Walt Disney poster advertising an Alice in Wonderland cartoon (c 1926) was acquired for over $7,000.00.

The posters in this book represent a cross-section of graphic illustrations advertising pre-cinema "moving picture" entertainments through the period of the early talking pictures. They are not photographic reproductions but, like the original posters, are completely hand-drawn. While some liberty has been taken in regards to the proportionate size of the original poster to accommodate the page size, every poster has been accurately rendered. Several of the posters (THE GREAT TRAIN ROBBERY, QUO VADIS) have been reworked from newspaper advertisements.

Rex Schneider has completely redesigned posters for A LA CONQUETE DU POLE, INTOLERANCE, NOSFERATU, THE ADVENTURES OF ACHMED and THE PHANTOM OF THE OPERA, for which the originals have either vanished or were not available for perusing. In each case, however, the scenes depicted and the atmosphere of the movies have been authentically recreated, and the style of lettering is that employed in the original design.

Of course, the inimitable Schneider style is clearly apparent, and with all due respect to the original artists, his personality portraits of Charlie Chaplin, Mabel Normand, Larry Semon and Gloria Swanson often surpass the initial illustrations.

Coloring the posters is great fun, but it is important to use only the finest materials. Color pencils of good quality are best. Felt pens are fine as long as they do not contain permanent ink that can bleed through the pages. Water-based felt pens are desirable for lettering.

For authenticity, use bright, circusy colors for pre-turn-of-the-century posters; slightly subdued colors for those from 1900-1914; pastel colors for Art Nouveau and bold, but subtle rich hues for Art Deco. The balance of the posters can be colored any way you like.

Happy poster-coloring!

CHRIS BUCHMAN

THE POSTERS

CINÉMATOGRAPHE LUMIÉRE (1896)

Frenchmen Louis and Auguste Lumiére were pioneers in the manufacture of motion picture cameras and projectors in the 1890s. In 1895 they became the first persons to project movies successfully. A reproduction of the original poster by M. Auzolle illustrating *A Practical Joke on the Gardener,* one of the ten short films of the Cinématographe Lumiére programme presented at London's Empire Theatre during 1896.

PHONO-CINÉMA-THÉÂTRE (1900)

"Talking" pictures have been around since the beginning of the movies, usually produced by combining the motion picture camera-projector and various phonographic processes. "*The Phono-Cinéma-Théâtre*" was a special exhibit at the Paris Exposition of 1900 showing "talking" pictures exclusively. Included on the program were Sarah Bernhardt and Coquelin Ainé in scenes from *Hamlet* and *Cyrano de Bergerac* as well as other Music Hall artistes. Reproduction of original poster.

THE GREAT TRAIN ROBBERY (1903)

Directed by Edwin S. Porter for the (Thomas) Edison Film Manufacturing Company, *The Great Train Robbery* has often been credited as the first American movie to illustrate a complete story. While this assumption is incorrect, Porter's film was probably the first to present the narrative through a succession of individually efdective scenes. The picture, a western, was photographed in the wilds of New Jersey. The poster is based on an advertisement appearing in trade journals of the period. The bandit was played by George Barnes, who fired point-blank at the audience during the opening and closing shots in the film.

AFGRUNDEN (THE ABYSS) (Denmark, 1910)

Danish actress Asta Nielsen specialized in tragic roles such as *Hamlet*. She was the first star to receive international recognition and was rated the most popular actress of 1911. By 1912, Nielsen was the highest-paid movie star in the world, receiving approximately $1,500 per week.

THE SQUAW'S LOVE (1911)

An early picture directed by D. W. Griffith, with Mabel Normand as Wild Flower. The letters AB are the trademark of the American Biograph Company, producers of the film. Pioneer film-makers inserted their trademarks into key scenes of pictures to thwart unauthorized print duplication by notorious film "pirates."

QUO VADIS (Italy, 1912)

Lengthy films were successfully produced in Europe years before D. W. Griffith made *The Birth of a Nation* in twelve reels. Enrico Guazzoni's eight-reel version of *Quo Vadis* was spectacular, featuring a cast of thousands, presented with orchestral musical accompaniment. The poster is based on advertisements from American and Swedish releases of the picture. The caption reads: "There are no less than 5000 people and 30 Lions."

À LA CONQUÊTE DU PÔLE (THE CONQUEST OF THE POLE) (France; 1912)

Frenchman George Méliès was the movies' first creative genius. A former magician, Méliès' fantasy films were an extension of his training in the "Theatre of Illusion." Incorporating most of the cinematic tricks we take for granted today (stop-motion photography, fades, dissolves, animation), Méliès conjured up hundreds of optical spectacles between 1896 through 1912. Many of these short films were hand-painted in a variety of colors. À LA CONQUÊTE DU PÔLE was one of Méliès' last efforts, based on Jules Verne's THE SPHINX OF THE ICE-FIELDS (1897). The poster represents the film's most famous scene.

HIS MAJESTY, THE SCARECROW OF OZ (1914)

L. Brank Baum, author of the popular "Oz" books, plays and musicals, formed the Oz Film Manufacturing Company in 1914, producing three movies from his celebrated tales.

(There were six films in all: three by the Selig Film Company, and three by Baum.) *His Majesty, the Scarecrow of Oz*, full of wonderful magical effects, was the last of the series. A facsimile of John R. Neill's original illustration reproduces the authentic lettering of the original poster.

THE PRICE OF SILENCE (1916)

An exact reproduction of the original Art Nouveau poster. The film featured Lon Chaney, Sr., make-up artist extraordinaire, in one of his early screen appearances.

INTOLERANCE (1916)

Subtitled "Love's Struggle Through the Ages." Director D. W. Griffith paralleled four separate historical stories dealing with political and religious intolerance. During the course of the fourteen-reel epic, the fates of Christ (The Judean Story), the Huguenots (The Medieval French Story) the Fall of Babylon, and the young lovers (The Modern Story) are interwoven, coming to a suspense-filled climax in the last reel. It was, and is, a masterpiece of Cinema Art.

CHARLOT (portrait, c. 1917)

Portraits of immensely popular film personalities, like Charlie Chaplin, were the only advertisements necessary to lure patrons into cinemas. Based on an original French poster.

MABEL NORMAND (portrait, c. 1917)

This character-portrait of Mabel Normand was all that was required to attract audiences into theatres showing her pictures. A beautiful woman, and a natural comedienne, Mabel Normand played in many early Charlie Chaplin comedies and later starred in her own feature movies. Facsimile of original poster.

BABES IN THE WOODS (1917)

This is an enchanting photoplay loosely adapted from the fairy tale *Hansel and Gretel.* Produced by William Fox, it was one of a series of movies especially designed for children. Facsimile of original poster.

CLEOPATRA (1917)

Theda Bara was the first American actress to be called a "vamp," short for vampirish ways. The mysterious Miss Bara vampired her way to stardom in *A Fool There Was* (1916) and went on to be perfectly cast as the temptress Cleopatra. Reproduction of original poster.

THE SINKING OF THE LUSITANIA (1918)

Winsor McCay was a newspaper illustrator and creator of the popular comic-strip character, "Little Nemo." He pioneered the animated cartoon in America, first hand-drawing a Nemo adventure, then inventing a cute dinosauur named Gertie. McCay toured in vaudeville, conversing from the stage to the animated Gertie on the movie screen. Unlike later cartoons, where character and background art are drawn on separate sheets of celluloid, McCay drew Gertie's movements and the still backgrounds, over and over, on single sheets of paper; there are over 9,000 individual pictures in the Gertie film. *The Sinking of the Lusitania* was similarly drawn. McCay's meticulous care for detail, and his intricate yet smooth animation, have rarely been equaled.

DAS CABINET DES DR. CALIGARI (THE CABINET OF DR. CALIGARI) (Germany; 1919)

A bizarre tale of a pair of youthful lovers, a carnival mesmerist and his zombie-like somnambulist. The story is visualized — as we discover in the film's final moments — through the eyes of the young man, a lunatic. The eccentric expressionistic sets were purposely designed to create a nightmarish atmosphere of the mad man's weird narrative. The poster is based on the original by Otto Stahl-Arpke, reflecting the mood of the picture accurately.

DR. JEKYLL AND MR. HYDE (1920)

Robert Louis Stevenson's gothic tale has been filmed a dozen times over. John Barrymore gave an amusingly sinister performance as Mr. Hyde, Dr. Jekyll's alter-ego in this aesthetically eerie adaptation. Reproduction of original poster.

THE COLD DECK (c 1920)

This western drama featured William S. Hart, whose sensitive portrayals of honest and incorruptible cowboy folk made him the movies' first real western hero. Through the use of realistic settings and believable plots, Hart's westerns were popular with adults and youngsters internationally. A former dramatic stage actor, Hart adopted the middle initial "S," which reputedly stands for "Shakespeare."

THE ADVENTURES OF TARZAN (1920)

Edgar Rice Burrough's *Tarzan* stories have been filmed 83 times. Elmo Lincoln was the first "ape-man" in TARZAN OF THE APES (1918), and in two later films, of which *The Adventures of Tarzan*, a thirteen-chapter serial, was his last. Based on original poster.

SALOME (1922)

This Oscar Wilde retelling of the fate of John the Baptist at the hands of Solome is one of the most aesthetically exuberant "art" films ever conceived or produced. The stylized costumes and sets, by Natacha Rambova (Mrs. Rudolph Valentino), were rendered in black, white, silver and gold, and based on Aubrey Beardsley's Art Nouveau illustrations. Salome was interpreted by Russian actress Alla Nazimova. The poster is a reworking of the original, combined with a facsimile of Beardsley's illustration from the book.

NOSFERATU, EINE SYMPHONIE DES GRAUENS (NOSFERATU, A SYMPHONY OF HORROR) (Germany, 1922)

This was the second screen version of Bram Stoker's novel DRACULA featuring Max Schreck as the carnivorous ratlike vampire. The film is filled with a haunting atmosphere which continues to evoke chills fifty-nine years later. This was the first major success of the brilliant young director Friedrich W. Murnau.

LARRY SEMON (portrait; c 1923)

Larry Semon was a giant among his contemporaries, whose comedies rivaled those of Buster Keaton and Charlie Chaplin. He was a marvelous acrobat, as well as an extremely clever writer and creator of complex sight gags. Semon wore a white face in most of his early films, this being a throwback to the tradition of white-faced clowns he'd seen and drawn in his youth. The films of Larry Semon are largely forgotten today, but whenever they are screened, audiences are convulsed with laughter.

DIE ABENTEUER DES PRINZEN ACHMED (THE ADVENTURES OF PRINCE ACHMED) (Germany, 1923-1926)

Employing the intricate silhouette technique of the Eastern Shadow Theatre, Lotte Reineger and husband Carl Koch produced this fully animated version of stories from the *Arabian Nights*. Photographed in an early color process, it remains the only feature-length movie of its kind.

THE THIEF OF BAGDAD (1924)

Douglas Fairbanks Sr. wrote and starred in this remarkable visualization of the *Arabian Nights* fantasy. Fairbanks' overwhelmingly winning personality, combined with his prowess for acrobatics, won the hearts of movie audiences throughout the world. Costing over two million dollars to produce, the film is a feast for the eyes, containing many exciting special-effect sequences. The poster is based on the original by Anton Grot, who assisted the illustrious William Cameron Menzies with the magnificent set designs.

FELIX TRIES TO REST (c. 1924)

Felix the Cat was probably the first cartoon character to gain prominence internationally. Although his name never appeared on posters and film title cards, it was Otto Messmer, not Pat Sullivan (the producer), who created, wrote and animated the Felix cartoons. By the mid-1920s, the devilish black cat had become so popular that Felix toys and other merchandise flooded the market.

SALLY OF THE SAWDUST (1925)

Comedian extraordinaire W. C. Fields appeared in the 1923 Broadway success POPPY, of which SALLY OF THE SAWDUST is the first of two screen adaptations. As Professor

Eustace McGargle, medicine-show faker, the film presents Fields' phenomenal juggling routine. The director was D. W. Griffith.

CLASH OF THE WOLVES (1925)
Rin Tin Tin was an ex-Army dog who appeared in a highly successful series of pictures from 1916 through the mid 1930s. In *Clash of the Wolves,* "Rinty" is rescued from a pack of wolves and, in turn, saves his master from a bunch of assorted bad guys.

BRONENOSETS POTEMKIN (THE BATTLESHIP POTEMKIN) (Russia, 1925)
THE BATTLESHIP POTEMKIN was the only part of a proposed lengthy epic about the 1905 Russian revolution. It is the story of an isolated incident concerning the circumstances and eventual outcome surrounding a rebellious mutiny on board the cruiser Potemkin. The film is a milestone of narrative cinematic devices,from the pacing of the visual construction, to the excitingly edited montage sequences. Time has not lessened its important contributions to film culture, nor has its impact been equaled. Genius Sergei M. Einsenstein directed and edited the picture. The poster is a reproduction of the original Soviet reissue of the film in 1929 by Vladimir and Gyorgy Sternberg.

THE PHANTOM OF THE OPERA (1925)
The first and most enduring of the three film versions of the macabre tale by Gaston Leroux. Lon Chaney Sr. (who plays Erik, the Phantom) was a master of the art of pantomime as well as a remarkable make-up artist. His innumerable character roles earned Chaney the designation of "the Man of a Thousand Faces." *The Phantom of the Opera* contained many scenes in the full Technicolor process of the period. The director was Rupert Julian.

THE LOST WORLD (1925)
Sir Arthur Conan Doyle's thrilling adventure-story of prehistoric beasts in the twentieth century. The culminating events of a captured brontosaurus brought back to civilization, where it escapes to create havoc, became the formula for countless later horror movies. The animals were created and animated by Willis O'Brien and his close associates, who later made KING KONG (1933) and MIGHTY JOE YOUNG (1949). Reproduction of original poster.

THE SON OF THE SHEIK (1926)
This is a sequel to Rudolph Valentino's successful 1921 picture, *The Sheik.* Portraying both father and son, the youthful sheik falls in love with the daughter of the chief of a band of brigands. It was the matinee-idol lover's last movie; Valentino died within hours of the New York premier in 1926, to the dismay of millions of fans.

METROPOLIS (Germany, 1926)
The story of the conflict between wealthy capitalists who rule Metropolis, a mechanized city of the future, and the robotized workers who tend the giant machines far underground seems inconsequential when compared with the visual presentation, for it is the impressive Art Deco architecture of strong geometric patterns, and the extraordinary special effects, that are the real stars of the epic Germanic science-fiction masterpiece. Fritz Lang directed. Poster is based on the original.

MONEY TALKS (1926)
John Held Jr. epitomized the era of bootleg hootch and jazz-age babies of the "Roaring Twenties" through his marvelous illustrations for *Liberty, The New Yorker* and other popular magazines of the period. Held was commissioned by Metro-Goldwyn-Mayer (the producers) to create posters for several of the studio's productions including *Money Talks,* a prohibition gangster comedy with Ned Sparks.

IRENE (1926)
This is the first screen version of the dazzling Broadway musical of the late teens. Its "3 Great Shows In One" refers to 1) a gorgeous fashion show in full color, 2) a human drama, sprinkled with chuckling comedy, and 3) a dainty but beautiful comedy performance by Colleen Moore as Irene. The Broadway songs by Tierney and McCarthy were incorporated into the film score and played by an orchestra from the pit during the showing of the movie.

THE GENERAL (1926)

Buster Keaton's "deadpan" expression, his comedic genius, and his physical dexterity as an acrobat, made him one of this century's most uproarious funnymen. *The General* is a comedy set in Civil War times. There are brilliant moments of hilarious sight gags, especially between Confederate engineer Buster, and his train, known as The General. After fifty-five years, the film still rates among the top ten throughout the world.

LONG FLIV THE KING (1926)

Audiences loved the comedies of Charley Chase. The character Chase developed was that of the plain and simple everyday "average man," caught in the midst of some domestic entanglement. A superb gag man with an exceptional genius for comedic invention, Chase wrote and directed many of the Hal Roach shorts of the 1930s under his real name, Charles Parrott. The films of Baltimore-born Charley Chase are now receiving the recognition they deserve. LONG FLIV THE KING was an elaborate and complex costume comedy in two reels. Facsimile of original advertisement.

WINGS (1927)

The picture concerns two World War I aviation pilots in love with the same woman, played by Clara Bow of 'It' fame. The film is notable for its impressively staged air battles and dog fights, some of which were shown in Magnascope, an early wide-screen process. Poster is reproduction.

GLORIA SWANSON (portrait, c 1928)

Of all the sustaining beauties of the Silver Screen, Gloria Swanson has been the most legendary for over fifty-three years, still going strong in the 1980s. This portrait, one of hundreds, is a facsimile of one which appeared on the cover of a popular movie magazine of the late 1920s.

A WOMAN OF AFFAIRS (1928)

Greta Garbo and John Gilbert were teamed in several successful box-office triumphs during the late 1920s. Rumors of an off-screen romance have persisted to this day among some closeted film historians, but in spite of this myth, the two were simply close friends. Poster based on the original.

TWO TARS (1928)

The films of Stan Laurel and Oliver Hardy have played consistently every day of every year throughout the world, since they were released. No other comedy team, single comedian, or comedienne has caused audiences to laugh on a more continual basis than these two funny men. In *Two Tars,* sailors Stan and Ollie manage to systematically wreck an entire line of automobiles during a traffic jam, on a lonely country road, on a blissful Sunday afternoon.

THE COCOANUTS (1929)

The Marx Brothers' (Harpo, Chico, Groucho, Zeppo) first film is a reworking of their 1925 Broadway success. It was one of Paramount Pictures' first "All Talking-All Singing-All Dancing" movies. The poster contains illustrations from the original movie and Broadway editions of the show.

LAILA (Norway, 1929)

The entire history of the Norwegian silent-film industry is recounted in but 50 movies, of which less than half survive. LAILA is the story of an infant (Laila) who is saved from the mouths of wolves by a man named Jampa, who then raises her as his own. Mona Mårtenson played Laila. The film was the next-to-last Norwegian silent movie.

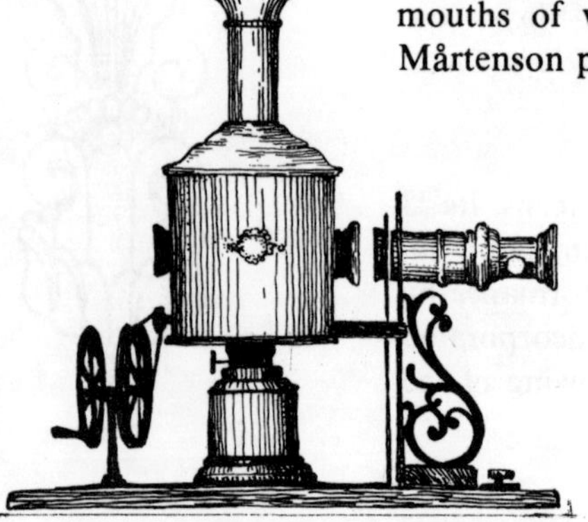

Chris Buchman

CINÉMATOGRAPHE
LUMIÈRE

Phono-Cinéma-Théâtre
Rue de Paris
à l'Exposition de 1900
FOOTIT ET CHOCOLAT
Intermède Comique
COSSIRA DE L'OPÉRA
Air de "Romeo et Juliette"
L'ENFANT PRODIGUE
3 TABLEAUX
PAR Melle Félicia MALLET
LITTLE TICH
Celébre Comique
POLIN
(Chanson)
"La Boiteuse du Regiment"
CYRANO DE BERGERAC
Scéne du Duel
PAR
COQUELIN AINÉ
HAMLET
Scéne du Duel
PAR
SARAH BERNARDT

EDISON FILMS

THE GREAT TRAIN ROBBERY

Asta Nielsen

„AFGRUNDEN"

THE SQUAW'S LOVE
AB

QUO VADIS?

**vari ej mindre än 5000 människor och
30 lejon medverkat.**

À la Conquête du Pôle

THE OZ FILM COMPANY PRESENTS

BLUEBIRD
PHOTOPLAYS PRESENT
THE DRAMA OF A WOMAN WHO TRUST-
ED AND THE PRICE SHE PAID!
"THE PRICE OF SILENCE"
WITH DOROTHY PHILLIPS & LON CHANEY
FROM THE STORY BY W. CAREY WONDERLY
DIRECTED BY JOSEPH DE GRASSE

D.W. GRIFFITH'S
COLOSSAL SPECTACLE
INTOLERANCE
A SUN PLAY OF THE AGES

EVEREST FILMS
PRÉSENTE
NEW YORK PARIS LONDON
EVEREST FILMS
BERLIN VIENNA BRUSSELS
CHARLOT

TRIANGLE
KEYSTONE

MABEL NORMAND

K

WILLIAM FOX
PRESENTS
THE
BABES IN THE WOODS

WILLIAM FOX *PRESENTS*

Theda Bara

-IN-

CLEOPATRA

BY

WINSOR McCAY

DAS CABINET DES Dr. CALIGARI

SECHS AKTE VON
KARL MAYER
UND HANS JANOWITZ
REGIE: ROBERT WIENE

STAHL
ARPKE

Adolph Zukor presents
JOHN
BARRYMORE
in
DR. JEKYLL AND
MR. HYDE
A PARAMOUNT ARTCRAFT PICTURE

S·A·LYNCH ENTERPRISES, INC.
PRESENT
WM S·HART
IN
THE COLD DECK
A SUPERLATIVE PRODUCTION

"ADVENTURES
OF
TARZAN"
Starring
ELMO LINCOLN
The Wild Animal Serial Supreme
with hundreds of animals ~
in 15 ELECTRIFYING
EPISODES ~
"THE TARZAN OF TARZANS"

NAZIMOVA
in Oscar Wilde's
"Salomé"
Direction By CHARLES BRYANT
sets & costumes by NATACHA RAMBOVA
photographed By CHARLES VAN ENGER
scenario By PETER M. WINTERS

Nosferatu,
eine Symphonie
des Grauens.
REGIE: F. W. MURNAU
IN DER HAUPTROLLE: MAX SCHRECK

LARRY SEMON

The Adventures of Prince Achmed

An animated film by Lotte Reineger

Douglas
Fairbanks
"THE THIEF OF BAGDAD"

FELIX
TRIES TO REST
A PAT SULLIVAN COMIC
M. J. WINKLER
DISTRIBUTOR, N.Y.

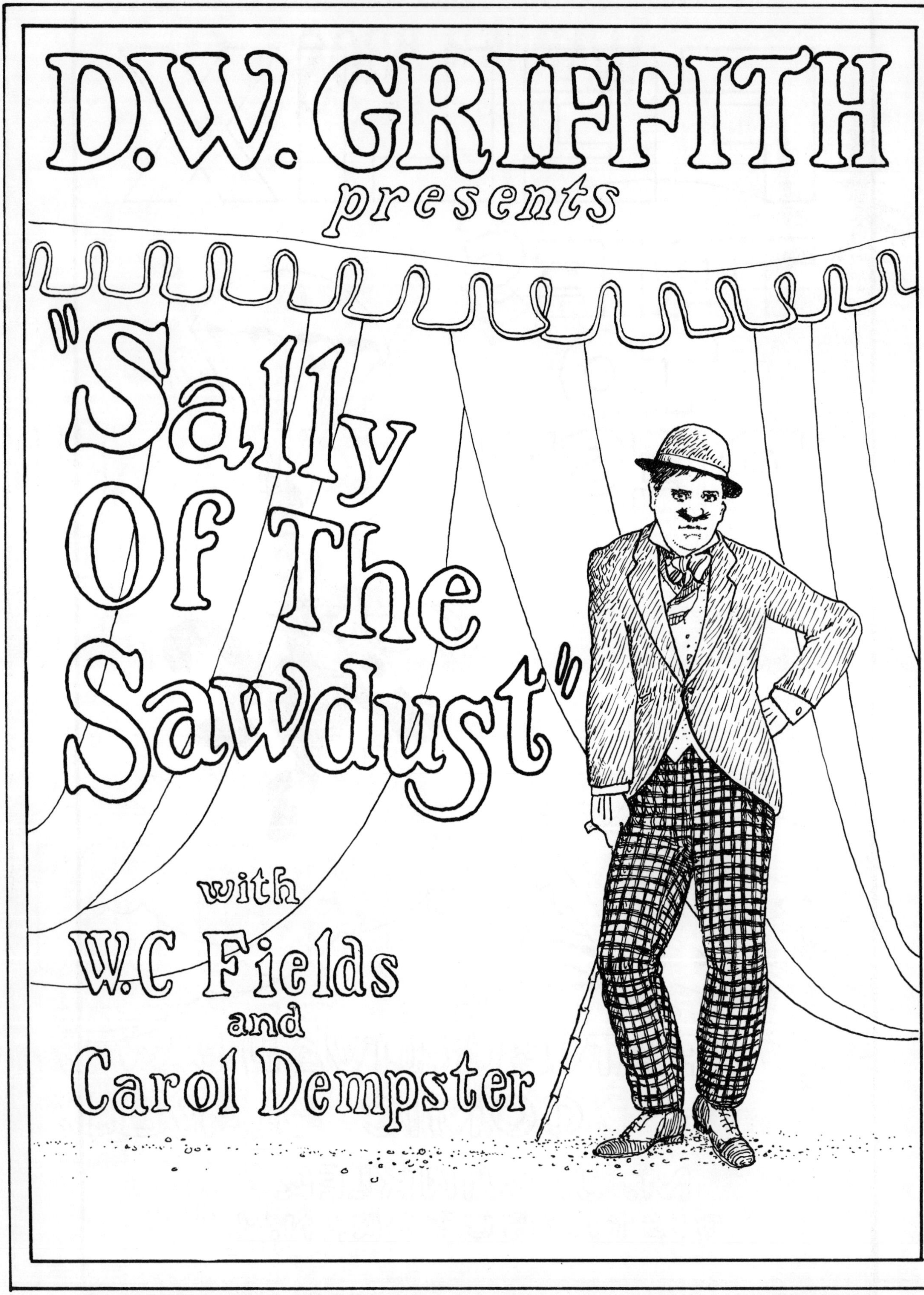

D.W. GRIFFITH

presents

"Sally Of The Sawdust"

with

W.C Fields

and

Carol Dempster

WARNER BROS.
PRESENTS
"The CLASH OF THE WOLVES"
With
RIN-TIN-TIN
JUNE MARLOWE
and CHARLES FARRELL
A story of man's
treachery and a wolf's
loyalty.

БРОНЕНОСЕЦ
ПОТЕМКИН
Режиссер - С.М. ЭЙЗЕНШТЕЙН. Оператор-ЭДУАРД ТИССЭ.
ПРОИЗВОДСТВО СОВКИНО

Carl
Laemmle
presents
The
phantom
of the
Opera
featuring
LON CHANEY
MARY PHILBIN
NORMAN
KERRY
DIRECTED BY RUPERT JULIAN
A UNIVERSAL PICTURE

FIRST NATIONAL PICTURES
The LOST WORLD
Sir A. Conan Doyle's Stupendous Story
with
BESSIE LOVE
LEWIS STONE
LLOYD HUGHES
WALLACE BEERY

John W. Considine, Jr. presents
RUDOLPH IN VALENTINO
"The Son of the Sheik"
a sequel to "The Sheik"
With VILMA BANKY

METROPOLIS
EIN FILM VON FRITZ LANG
UFA
JN DEN HAUPTROLLEN
BRIGITTE HELM - GUSTAV FRÖHLICH
ALFRED ABEL, RUDOLPH KLEIN ROGGE, THEODOR LOOS, FRITZ RASP, HEINRICH GEORGE
AN DER KAMERA
KARL FREUND, GÜNTHER RITTAU

MONEY TALKS

Directed by
ARCHIE MAYO

John McCormick presents
Colleen Moore
in
"Irene"
WITH
LLOYD HUGHES
GEORGE K. ARTHUR - CHARLEY MURRAY
Directed by
ALFRED E. GREEN
FILMED IN
ACTUAL COLOR
3 Great shows in one
First National Pictures

JOSEPH
M.
SCHENCK
presents
BUSTER KEATON
in
"The General"

WINGS
With CLARA BOW
CHARLES (Buddy) ROGERS, RICHARD ARLEN
and GARY COOPER

GLORIA SWANSON

JOHN GILBERT
GRETA GARBO
CLARENCE BROWN'S
PRODUCTION
A WOMAN OF AFFAIRS
With LEWIS STONE
JOHN MACK BROWN
DOUGLAS FAIRBANKS JR.
A Metro-Goldwyn-Mayer PICTURE

Hal Roach presents

STAN LAUREL
OLIVER HARDY
IN
"TWO TARS"

Paramount presents
The
MARX
BROTHERS
IN
THE
Cocoanuts
with
MARY EATON
and OSCAR SHAW
Music by IRVING BERLIN